Eleven Pieces for Piano

On The Cool Side

Brian Chapple

Chester Music Limited
A division of Music Sales Limited
8/9 Frith Street, London W1V 5TZ.

Performance Notes

Of the three pieces that swing (Nos. 1, 2 and 9) 'Walking The Dog' is
perhaps the crispest and wittiest, whilst 'Happy Days' is straightforwardly
bright and rhythmic (the loud final chord must be a surprise).
'Swing Slow' needs a light, sometimes quite 'punchy' touch with the
sophistication of Count Basie – don't rush this piece or be mean with the silences.

There are three slow pieces (5, 7 and 10). 'Sad Song' is the most deeply
expressive (*crescendo*, *diminuendo* and *rubato* may be generously employed).
'The Blue Pool' should ripple mysteriously – make strong contrast between the
accompaniment and the right hand *cantabile* tune that begins at the end of bar 7.
'On The Cool Side' needs to be freely flowing and expressive.

'Come Dancing' should be an affectionate parody of a tango (and the
BBC Television programme), whilst the two waltzes (4 and 6) need to
contain plenty of dramatic contrasts of colour. 'Washtub Rag' should be
boisterous and full of energy and fun.

B.C.

Brian Chapple

Brian Chapple lives just outside London, working as teacher and pianist as well as composer.
He has written a wide variety of music: earlier pieces tended to be 'quirky' ('Scherzos' for
four pianos and 'Green And Pleasant'), whilst recent pieces are more serious
('In Memoriam', 'Tribute' and 'Requies').

His daughter Rosalind suggested the title for 'Venus Fly Trap' – although she
had been hoping for a piece entitled 'Forty-four Daisies'!
The two volumes of piano pieces for children ('Lazy Days' and 'On The Cool Side')
were written with his pupils in mind.

Brian Chapple enjoys gardening, drawing, France and all things French.
At present he is completing a Mass.

Exclusive distributors:
Music Sales Limited
Newmarket Road, Bury St. Edmunds, Suffolk IP33 3YB

ISBN 0.7119.2687.5
Order No. CH59436

Printed in the United Kingdom by
Caligraving Limited, Thetford, Norfolk.

1. Happy Days

2. Walking The Dog

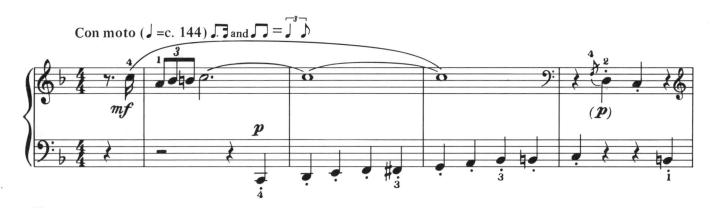

3. Parade

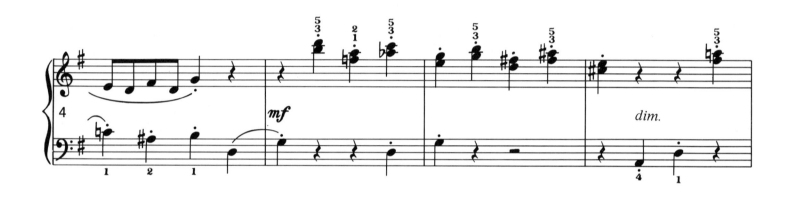

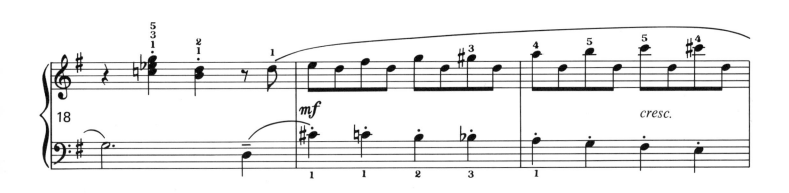

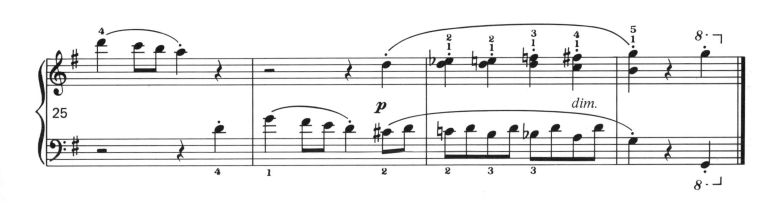

4. Valse Parisienne

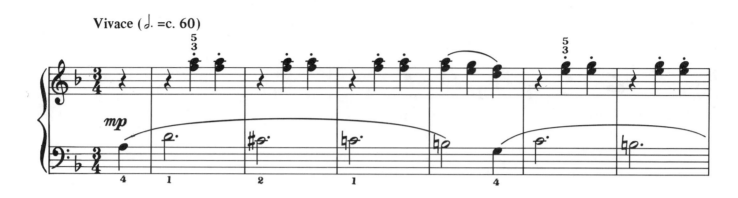

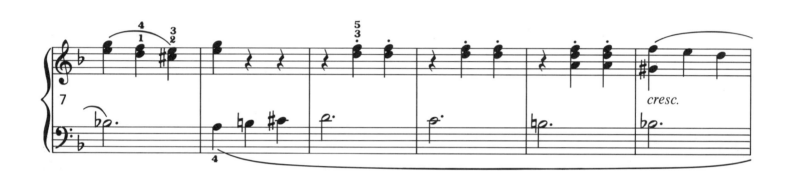

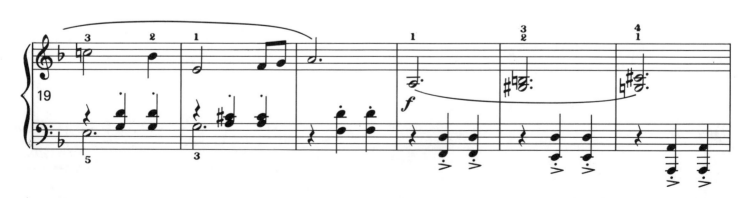

5. The Blue Pool

6. Tea With Aunt Maud

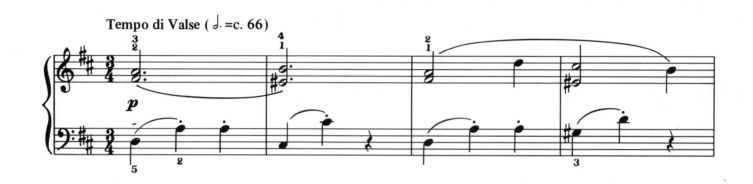

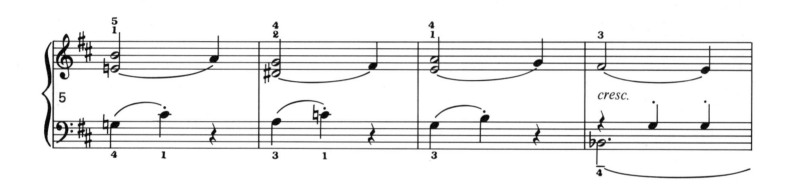

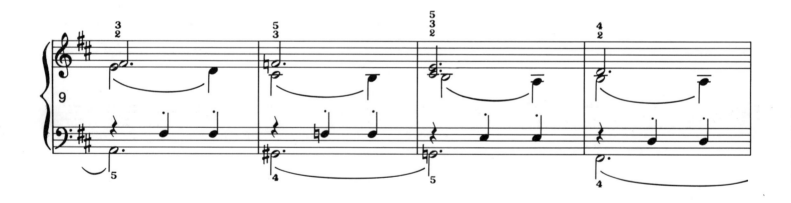

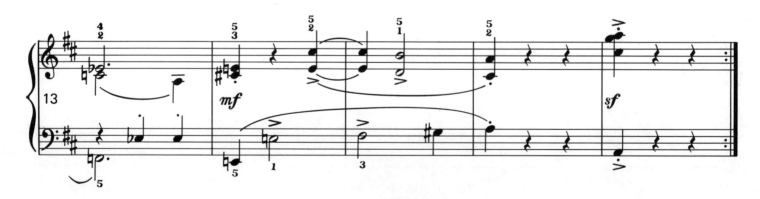

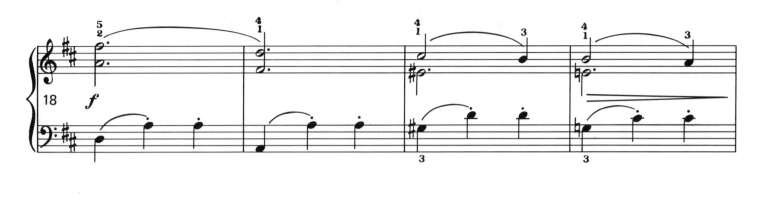

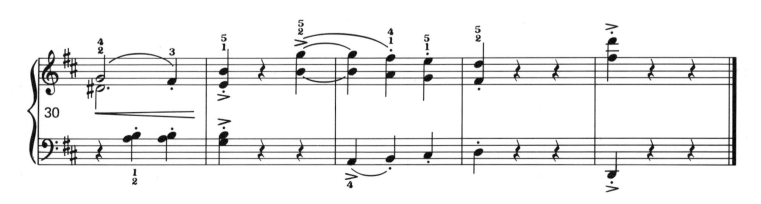

7. On The Cool Side

8. 'Come Dancing'

Andante elegantemente (♩ =c. 60)

9. Swing Slow

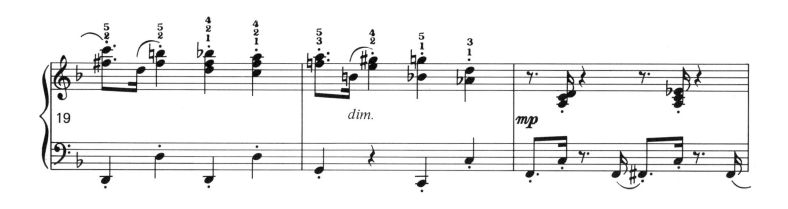

10. Sad Song

11. Washtub Rag

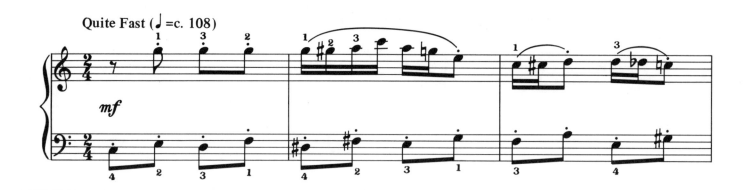

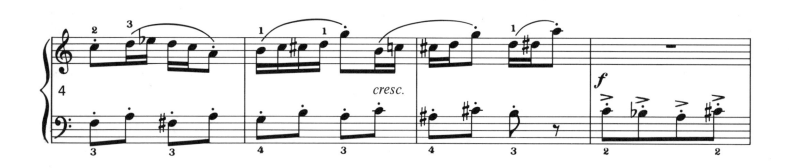

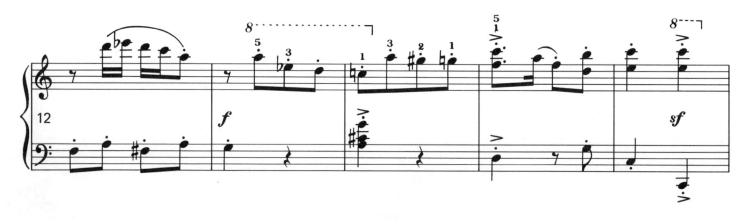

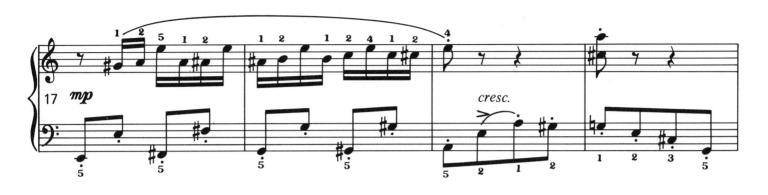

4/94 (17651)